Out of this World

Washed Away

Contents

by Keira Wong

illustrated by Douglas Fong

SCHOLASTIC

H A L Y C R U S

Reading Manga: What is it?

The Japanese word 'manga' has been used for nearly 200 years. It means whimsical pictures (man = whimsical, ga = pictures).

Today, manga is a label for Japanese-style graphic novels, comic books and animated movies (also called anime). What's the difference between a graphic novel and a comic book? The answer is in your hands. Graphic novels are usually quality productions, sometimes run to hundreds of pages, and often cover serious subjects. Many Japanese manga focus on topics like the environment, the law, science, history – you name it.

Manga don't all look exactly the same, but they have some things in common:

Big Eyes

Oversized Expressions

Fast Action

Reading Manga: How to Follow

Each page of a graphic novel is divided into boxes called panels. You follow the panels from left to right and top to bottom, like this:

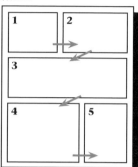

Each panel is like a paragraph in a regular book. It shows you where the characters are, and what they are doing, saying and thinking.

Some panels include a little box at the top (or the bottom), giving you information about what's going on. These are called captions.

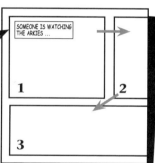

SOMEONE IS WATCHING THE ARKIES ...

DID YOU KNOW?

Traditional Japanese manga look a little different. That's because in Japan, people read from right to left. Japanese manga is read like this:

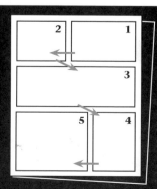

It's easier than it looks!

Reading Manga: Who's talking?

Speech balloons tell you who is speaking, what they're saying, and how.

Sometimes the lettering changes, to tell you which words are most important. These words might appear in **BOLD** or LARGE TYPE or in *ITALICS*.

Sometimes a punctuation point is enough to explain what's going on.

And how would you show an alien language? Maybe like this:

Reading Manga:
What's that sound?

When you read speech bubbles, you hear manga characters' voices inside your head. There's a way to hear the background noises too – the rumble of thunder, the ringing of a telephone, the crack of a stick underfoot.

Manga artists represent sound effects (or SFX) by placing words over the panels, using lettering to suit each particular sound. It looks like this:

Scary sound

Mechanical sound

Quiet sound

DID YOU KNOW?

Japanese manga SFX are very precise. For example, *bicha bicha* means small splash, *bashan* is a medium splash, and *zaban* is a very big splash. There's even an SFX for total silence: *shiin.*
SFX are used to show emotions as well. The word *unzori* placed next to a character tells you they're feeling bored. If it was *moji moji* they'd be feeling shy, and *shobo shobo* indicates sadness.

Reading Manga:

What's that look on your face?

Manga characters have exaggerated expressions, to help you understand what they're feeling. The first feature everyone notices is the eyes, which may be wide open in:

Shock

Fear

Hope

Closed eyes can mean:

Laughter

Sadness

Noses and chins are more difficult to spot (some characters have no nose at all). This reflects the Japanese preference for delicate features. In manga, big noses and chins are kept for the bad guys.

Reading Manga:

What's that look on your face?

Just like manga characters' eyes, manga mouths are either huge or tiny. A big, wide-open mouth indicates:

Fear

Anger

Happiness

A character with a little mouth may be feeling:

Sad

Thoughtful

Shy

You can also tell a lot about manga characters from the crazy colour or style of their hair. For example, blue hair can mean the character is cool-headed, while orange hair equals determination (and sometimes a fiery temper). Wild, spiky hairstyles show the character is adventurous.

Characters

Earthlings

Molly

Molly is sporty and adventurous, and friendly to everyone – even aliens from strange planets.

James

Molly's friend James is always ready for a new challenge. Just as well.

Halycrusians

Z-koo

A Halycrusian leader, who is honest, fair-minded and keen to explore his world with Molly and James.

K-la

Z-koo's niece. She doesn't always think before acting, and this can lead to trouble ...

B-roc

B-roc is a laid-back guy – always on the lookout for something to eat.

THE PORTAL TO ANOTHER WORLD COULD BE AS CLOSE AS YOUR LOCAL SCRAPYARD ... AS MOLLY AND JAMES ARE ABOUT TO DISCOVER!

C'MON, JAMES, YOU SAID WE COULD FIND SOME WOOD TO MAKE MY AUNT A JEWELLERY BOX. BUT ALL YOU'VE DONE IS LOOK AT JUNK.

I LOVE JUNK ...

BUT IF WE CARRY ALL THESE ... THINGS ... WE WON'T BE ABLE TO CARRY ALL THE WOOD.

I BET I CAN USE IT FOR SOMETHING.

I BOUGHT MY AUNT THIS EYESHADOW FROM THE PHARMACY, TOO. IT'S CALLED "LIME ICE".

UH, YEAH ...

JAMES AND MOLLY START TO EXPLORE THE STRANGE LAND, SEARCHING FOR A WAY BACK TO EARTH.

THESE ROCKS ARE REALLY WEIRD. IT LOOKS LIKE THERE ARE JEWELS INSIDE!

WE'VE GOT TO FIND A WAY BACK HOME ... BUT I GUESS WE COULD ENJOY OURSELVES WHILE WE'RE LOOKING.

SOUNDS GOOD!

THOSE JEWELLED ROCKS ARE EVERYWHERE! LOOK OVER THERE!

LET'S CHECK OUT THAT CANYON!

BUT THE CREATURE IS TOO FRIGHTENED OF JAMES TO ACCEPT HIS HELP.

AAAGH! WHAT'S THAT?

DON'T BE AFRAID. WE WANT TO HELP YOU.

WH-WHAT? HOW COME I CAN HEAR YOU ... IN MY HEAD?

YOU CAN HEAR OUR THOUGHTS, JUST AS WE CAN HEAR YOURS. DON'T SPEAK YOUR WORDS. THINK THEM, AND WE CAN UNDERSTAND EACH OTHER.

TAKE HOLD!

YOU CAN HEAR MY THOUGHTS? THEN LISTEN ... WE NEED TO SAVE JAMES!

I KNOW WHAT WE CAN DO. HERE'S THE PLAN ...

WHERE DID THAT YELLOW THING GO?

AH! THERE YOU ARE!

WHAT DO YOU WANT?

THIS DAY JUST KEEPS GETTING STRANGER. DID YOU JUST SPEAK TO ME INSIDE MY HEAD?

I HAVE TO GET AWAY FROM THIS THING!

THAT HAS TO BE YOUR VOICE INSIDE MY HEAD!

MOLLY IS RUSHING TO THE RESCUE.

YOU HAVE TO SEND YOUR THOUGHTS TO YOUR FRIEND. HE'LL RECOGNISE YOU. TELL HIM EXACTLY WHAT WE SAID.

JAMES! LIE FLAT ON YOUR BACK. POINT YOUR FEET DOWNSTREAM!

MOLLY?

IT WILL MAKE IT EASIER TO GRAB ON TO THAT CRACK IN THE WALL! AND YOU'LL STOP SPINNING!

WHAT'S GOING ON?

HALYCRUS WAS NOT ALWAYS SO DANGEROUS. IT IS SAID THAT IN OUR GRANDFATHERS' TIME, THESE FLASH FLOODS DID NOT HAPPEN.

BUT NOW ... AH WELL, WE KNOW A SAFE PASSAGE AROUND THE CANYON. WE SHOULD GO. YOU TOO K-LA!

WHAT'S THIS? IT SHIMMERS LIKE BEJAIS!

OH, MY AUNT'S GIFT!

YUCK. IT HAS ALL YOUR SCRAPYARD JUNK IN IT, JAMES!

JUST BEFORE WE CAME HERE ... HEY, MOLLY! I THINK I KNOW HOW TO GET HOME.

NOW THAT YOU KNOW WHAT TO DO, WILL YOU COME BACK TO HALYCRUS AGAIN?

OF COURSE! BUT WE MIGHT STAY AWAY FROM THE CANYON NEXT TIME! BYE!

BACK ON EARTH ...

WE MADE A PORTAL TO ANOTHER PLANET! I DON'T BELIEVE IT.

AND I THINK I KNOW HOW TO MAKE IT AGAIN!

AND THEY WERE ALL SO NICE ...

WELL ... ALL EXCEPT K-LA! SHE DIDN'T TRUST ME!

DO YOU THINK THIS OLD COMB WOULD BE A GOOD BIRTHDAY GIFT FOR YOUR AUNT NOW THAT THE EYESHADOW IS RUINED?

MAYBE K-LA DIDN'T WANT YOUR HELP BECAUSE SHE KNEW YOU WENT GIFT SHOPPING IN JUNK YARDS! THEY CAN READ MINDS, REMEMBER!

MOLLY AND JAMES WILL TRAVEL TO HALYCRUS AGAIN. AND ONE DAY, FAR IN THE FUTURE, OTHER KIDS MAY FIND THE PORTAL TO A VERY CHANGED HALYCRUS ...

Washed Away
Portalopedia

Bejais Jewel-like baubles found in rocks.

Can be made into almost anything. Also the

Halycrusians' only food.

Halycrus An alternative world.

Halycrusians Inhabitants of Halycrus.

Mind message A thought, sent to another

being to communicate.

Mind-reading The ability to hear another

being's thoughts.

Portal A doorway into an alternative world.

Hi Lo